The Easy Ke

Frank Sinatra

15 classic songs for keyboard

Come Fly With Me 2

Fly Me To The Moon 4

I Get A Kick Out Of You 6

I've Got You Under My Skin 8

Mack The Knife 10

My Kind Of Town (Chicago Is) 12

My Way 14

Nice 'n' Easy 16

Night And Day 18

Somethin' Stupid 20

Strangers In The Night 22

Summer Wind 24

The Lady Is A Tramp 26

Theme From New York, New York 28

They Can't Take That Away From Me 30

© International Music Publications Ltd
First published in 2001 by International Music Publications Ltd
International Music Publications Ltd is a Faber Music company
3 Queen Square, London WC1N 3AU

Cover image Michael Ochs Archive / Redferns Music Picture Library
Music arranged & processed by Barnes Music Engraving Ltd

Printed in England by Caligraving Ltd
All rights reserved

ISBN10: 0-571-52952-6
EAN13: 978-0-571-52952-0

Come Fly With Me

Words by Sammy Cahn / Music by James Van Heusen

Suggested Registration: Vibraphone
Rhythm: Swing
Tempo: ♩ = 128

Come fly with me, let's fly, __ let's fly a-way! __ If you can use some ex-

-ot-ic booze, there's a bar in far Bom-bay, come fly with me, let's fly, __ let's fly a - way!

__ Come fly with me, let's float __ down to Pe-ru! __ In

Lla - ma Land there's a one-man band, and he'll toot his flute for you, come

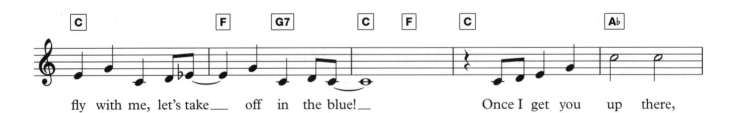

fly with me, let's take __ off in the blue! __ Once I get you up there,

where the air is ra - ri - fied, __ we'll just glide, __ star - ry-eyed. Once I get you

Warner/Chappell Music Ltd, London W6 8BS and The International Music Network Ltd, London E4 6PD

Fly Me To The Moon

Words and Music by Bart Howard

Suggested Registration: Vibraphone
Rhythm: Swing
Tempo: ♩ = 116

Fly me to the moon,__ and let me play a-mong the stars,__

let me see what Spring__ is like on Ju - pi - ter and Mars.__ In

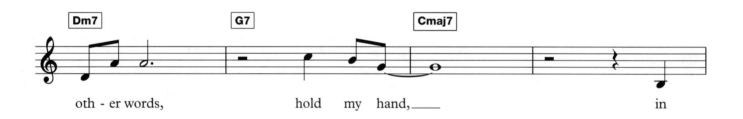

oth - er words, hold my hand,___ in

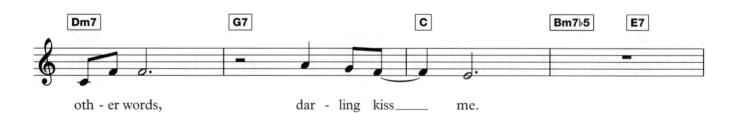

oth - er words, dar - ling kiss___ me.

Fill my heart with song,__ and let me sing for ev - er - more,__

you are all I long___ for, all I wor - ship, and a - dore.___ In

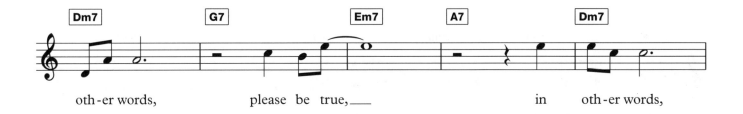

oth-er words,   please be true,___   in   oth-er words,

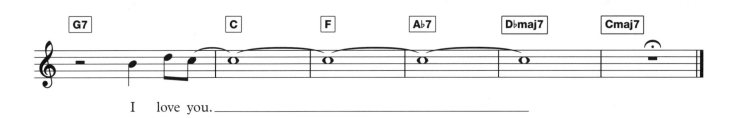

I   love you._____

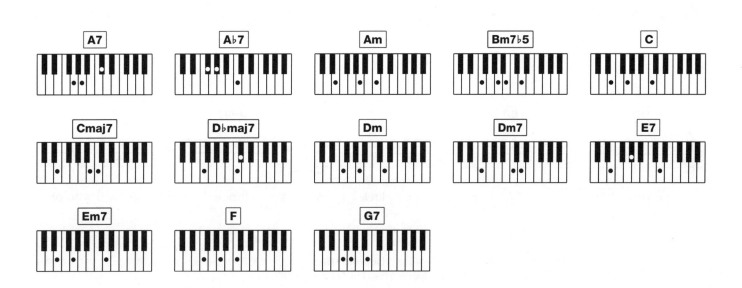

I Get A Kick Out Of You

Words and Music by Cole Porter

Suggested Registration: Vibraphone
Rhythm: Swing
Tempo: ♩ = 132 (♩ = 66 for melody)

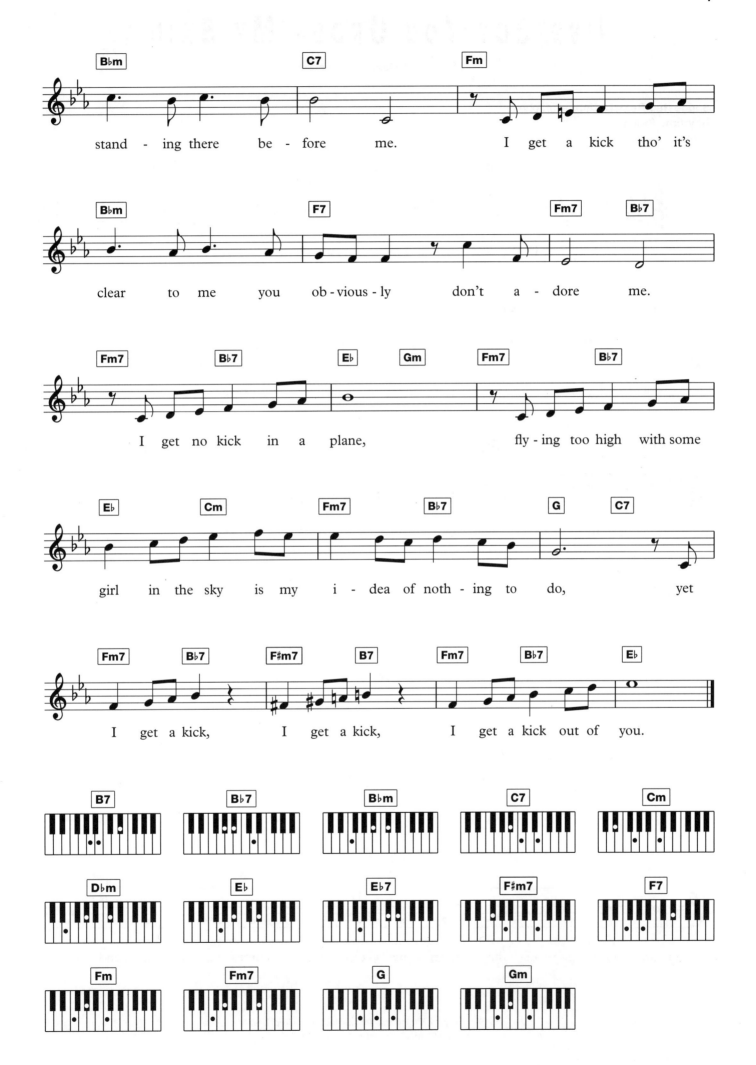

I'VE GOT YOU UNDER MY SKIN

Words and Music by Cole Porter

Suggested Registration: Vibraphone
Rhythm: Swing
Tempo: ♩ = 106

I've got you_____ un-der my skin,_____ I've

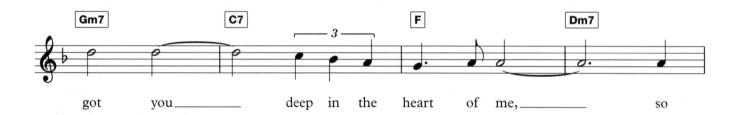

got you_____ deep in the heart of me,_____ so

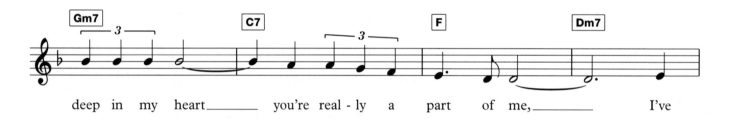

deep in my heart_____ you're real-ly a part of me,_____ I've

got you_____ un-der my skin._____ I'll

sac-ri-fice a-ny-thing, come what might, for the sake of hav-ing you

near, in spite of the warn-ing voice that comes in the night, and re-

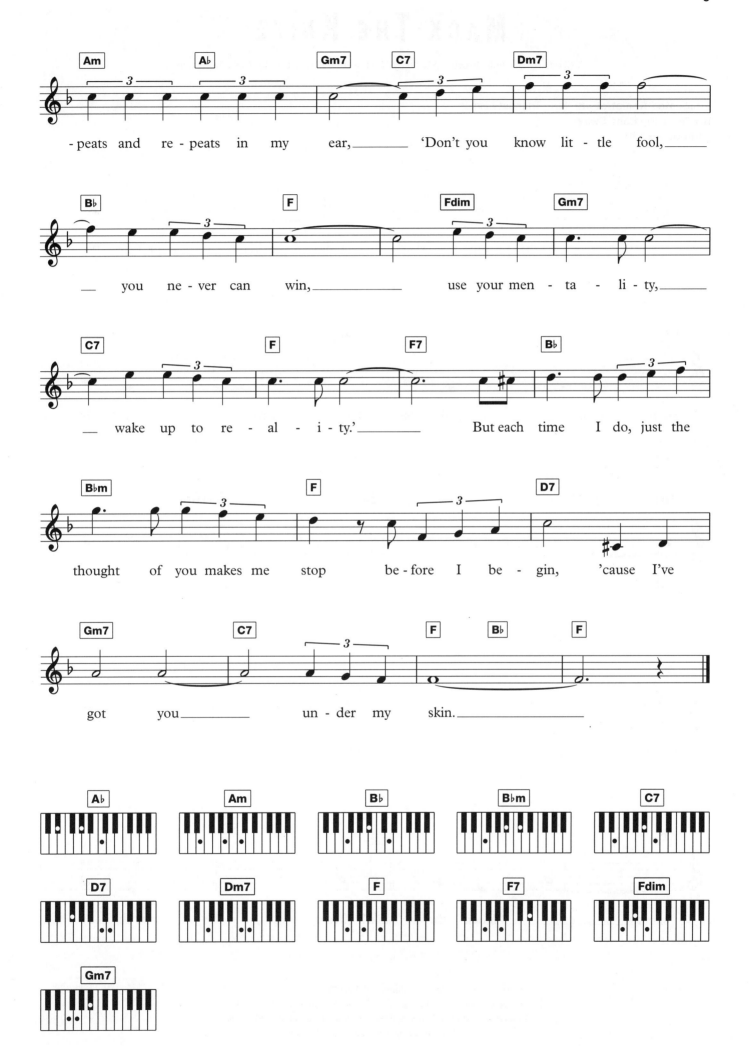

MACK THE KNIFE

Words by Berthold Brecht / Music by Kurt Weill / Translation by Marc Blitzstein

Suggested Registration: Solo Trumpet / Brass
Rhythm: Big Band Swing
Tempo: ♩ = 180

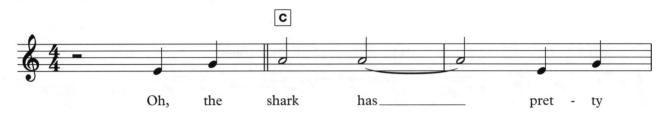

Oh, the shark has _____ pret - ty

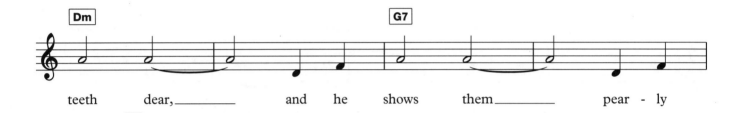

teeth dear, _____ and he shows them _____ pear - ly

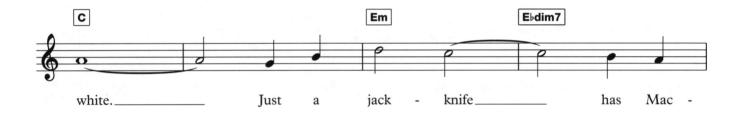

white. _____ Just a jack - knife _____ has Mac -

- heath dear, _____ and he keeps it _____ out of

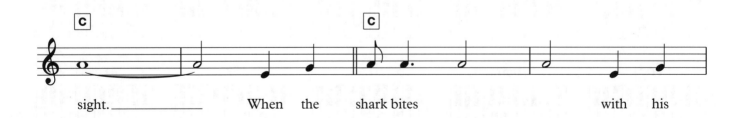

sight. _____ When the shark bites with his

teeth dear,   scar - let bil-loes   start to

spread.   Fan - cy gloves though,_____

_ wears Mac - heath_____ dear,_____ so there's

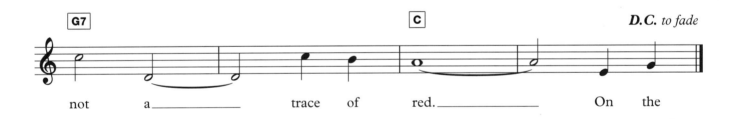

not a_____ trace of red._____ On the

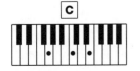
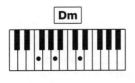
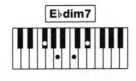
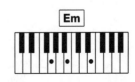
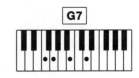

My Kind Of Town (Chicago Is)

Words by Sammy Cahn / Music by James Van Heusen

Suggested Registration: Vibraphone / Jazz Guitar
Rhythm: Swing
Tempo: ♩ = 180

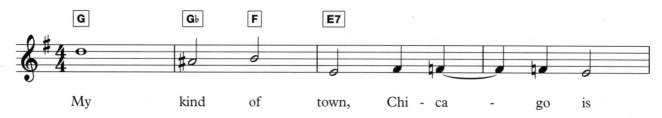

My kind of town, Chi - ca - go is

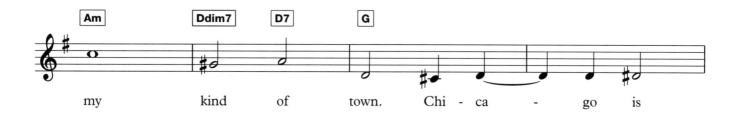

my kind of town. Chi - ca - go is

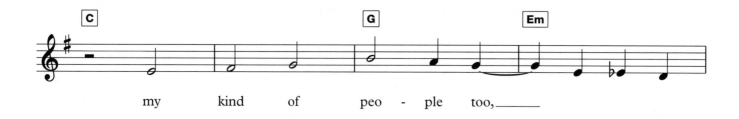

my kind of peo - ple too,_____

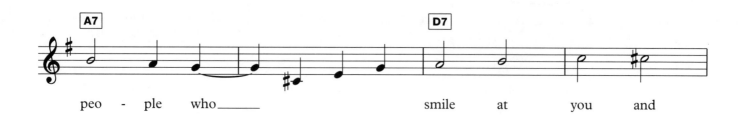

peo - ple who_____ smile at you and

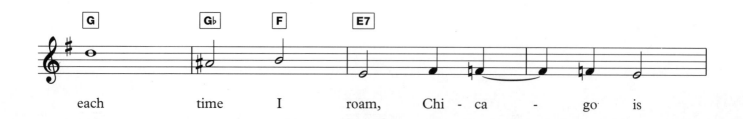

each time I roam, Chi - ca - go is

call - ing me home. Chi - ca - go is

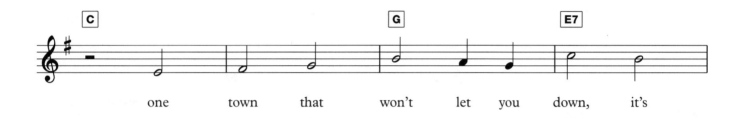

one town that won't let you down, it's

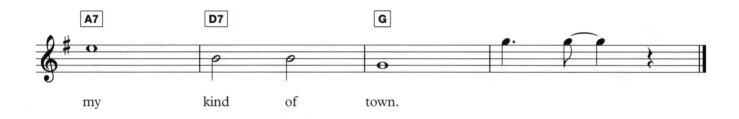

my kind of town.

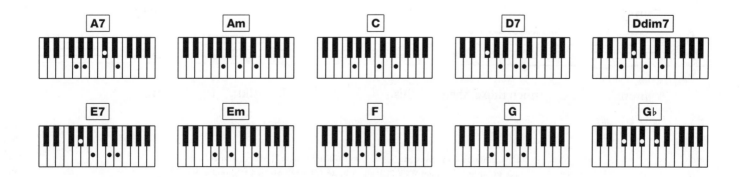

My Way

French Words by Gilles Thibaut / English Words by Paul Anka / Music by Claude François and Jacques Revaux

Suggested Registration: Strings
Rhythm: Soft Rock
Tempo: ♩ = 84

And

now_____ the end is near,_____ and so I face_____ the fi - nal

cur - tain,__ my friend,_____ I'll say it clear,_____ I'll state my

case,_____ of which I'm cer - tain.__ I've lived_____ a life that's

full,_____ I've trav-elled each_____ and ev - ery high - way,__ and

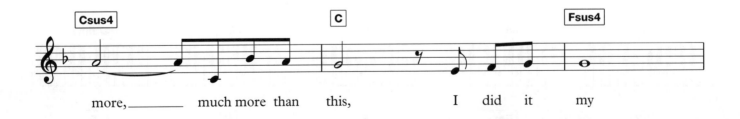

more,_____ much more than this, I did it my

way. Yes, there were times,_____ I'm sure you knew,_____ when I bit

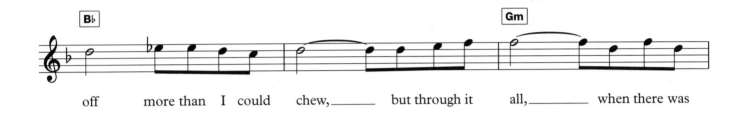

off more than I could chew,_____ but through it all,_____ when there was

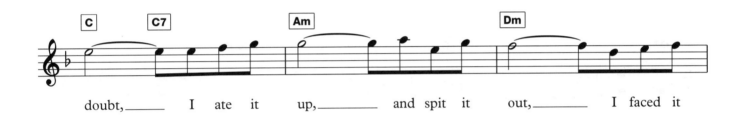

doubt,_____ I ate it up,_____ and spit it out,_____ I faced it

all,_____ and I stood tall,_____ and did it my way._____

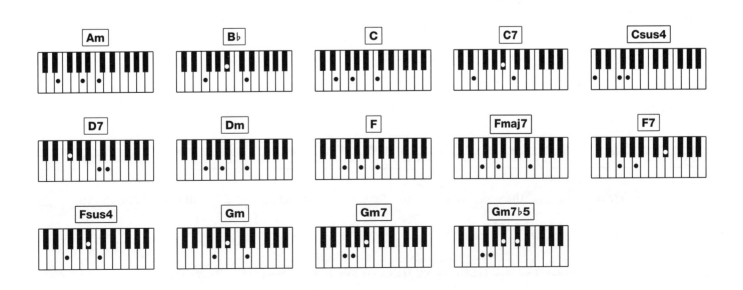

Nice 'N' Easy

Words by Alan Bergman and Marilyn Keith / Music by Lewis Spence

Suggested Registration: Piano / Vibraphone / Guitar
Rhythm: Swing
Tempo: ♩ = 100

Let's take it nice 'n' ea - sy, it's gon - na

be so ea - sy for us to fall in love. ___

Hey ba - by, what's your hur - ry?

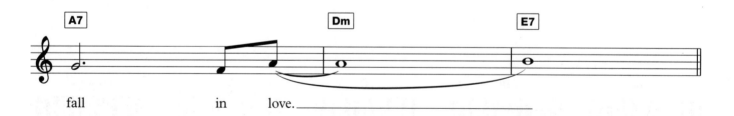

Re - lax and don't you wor - ry, we're gon - na

fall in love. _____

We're on the road to ro - mance, that's safe to

Night And Day

Words and Music by Cole Porter

Suggested Registration: Vibraphone
Rhythm: Medium Swing
Tempo: ♩ = 96

Night and day,_____ you are the one,

on - ly you be - neath the moon, and un - der the sun.

Whe - ther near to me or far, it's no mat - ter dar - ling

where you are,___ I think of you,___ night and day._____

___ Day and night,_____ why is it so,

that this long - ing for you fol - lows wher - ev - er I go?

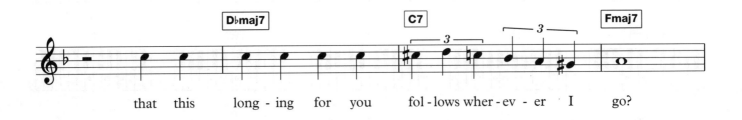

Somethin' Stupid

Words and Music by Carson Parks

Suggested Registration: Brass
Rhythm: Cha-Cha
Tempo: ♩ = 120

I know I stand in line un - til you think you have the time to spend the

eve-ning with me.___ And if we go some place to dance, I

know that there's a chance you won't be leav-ing with me.___ Then

af - ter-wards we drop in - to a qui - et lit - tle place and have a drink or two.___

And then I go and spoil it all by say-ing some-thing stu-pid like 'I

love you.'_____ I can see it in your eyes that you des - pise the same old lines you heard the

night be - fore.___ And though it's just a line to you, for

me it's true and ne - ver seemed so right be - fore. __ I

prac-tice ev - ery day to find some cle - ver lines to say to make the mean-ing come through.

But then I think I'll wait un - til the eve - ning is late and I'm a -

- lone with you. __ The time is right, your per-fume fills my

head, the stars get red, and oh, the night's so blue. __ And

then I go and spoil it all by say - ing some-thing stu - pid like 'I love you.' ____

__ 'I love you.' ____

Strangers In The Night

Words by Charles Singleton and Eddie Snyder / Music by Bert Kaempfert

Suggested Registration: Solo Trumpet / Oohs (Choir)
Rhythm: Beguine
Tempo: ♩ = 100

Summer Wind

German Words by Hans Bradtke / English Words by Johnny Mercer / Music by Henry Mayer

Suggested Registration: Vibraphone
Rhythm: Medium Swing
Tempo: ♩ = 100

The sum-mer wind came blow-in' in a - cross the sea,__

it ling-ered there to touch your hair, and walk with me.__

All sum-mer long we sang a song, and strolled the gold - en

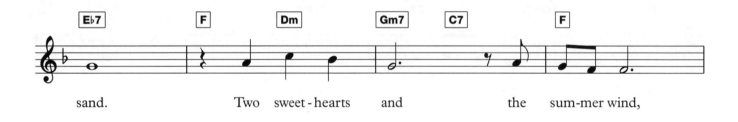

sand. Two sweet-hearts and the sum-mer wind,

like paint-ed kites the days and nights went fly-ing by.__

The world was new be - neath a blue um - brel - la sky,_

then soft - er than a pi - per man, one

day it called to you, I lost you to the

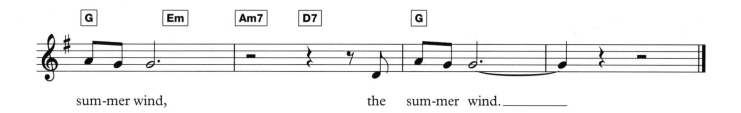

sum-mer wind, the sum-mer wind._____

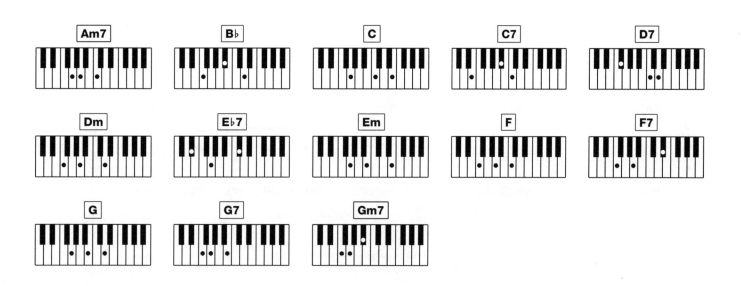

THE LADY IS A TRAMP

Words by Lorenz Hart / Music by Richard Rodgers

Suggested Registration: Saxophone
Rhythm: Swing
Tempo: ♩ = 132

I get too hun-gry for din-ner at eight,___

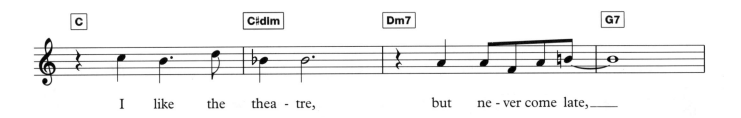

I like the thea-tre, but ne-ver come late,___

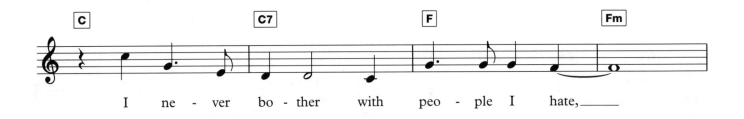

I ne-ver bo-ther with peo-ple I hate,_____

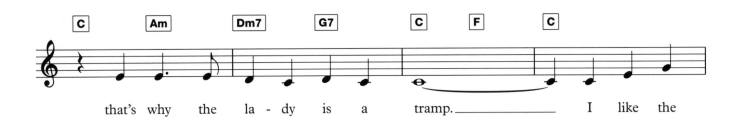

that's why the la-dy is a tramp._____ I like the

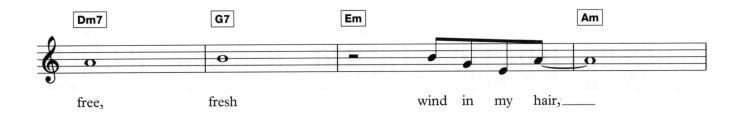

free, fresh wind in my hair;___

life with-out care,___ I'm broke, it's oke,

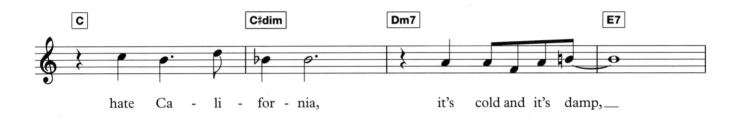

hate Ca - li - for - nia, it's cold and it's damp,___

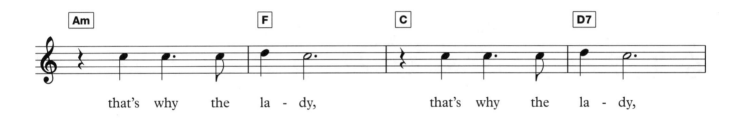

that's why the la - dy, that's why the la - dy,

that's why the la - dy is a tramp.___

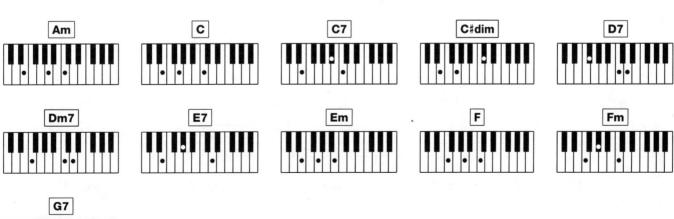

THEME FROM NEW YORK, NEW YORK

Words by Fred Ebb / Music by John Kander

Suggested Registration: Brass / Trumpet
Rhythm: Bounce / Swing
Tempo: ♩ = 110

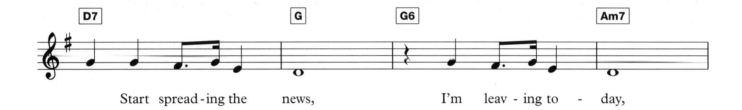

Start spread-ing the news, I'm leav-ing to - day,

I wan - na be a part of it, New York, New York.

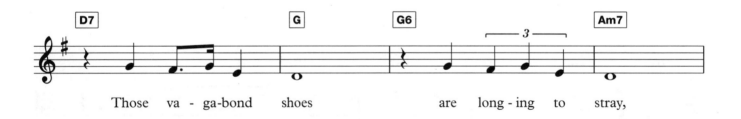

Those va - ga-bond shoes are long - ing to stray,

and step a - round the heart of it, New York, New York.

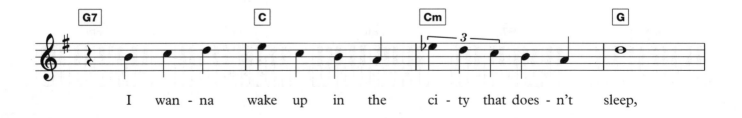

I wan - na wake up in the ci - ty that does - n't sleep,

THEY CAN'T TAKE THAT AWAY FROM ME

Music and Lyrics by George Gershwin and Ira Gershwin

Suggested Registration: Vibraphone
Rhythm: Swing
Tempo: ♩ = 112

The way you wear your hat, ____ the way you sip your tea, ____

the mem-'ry of all that. ____ No! No! They can't take that a-way from me.

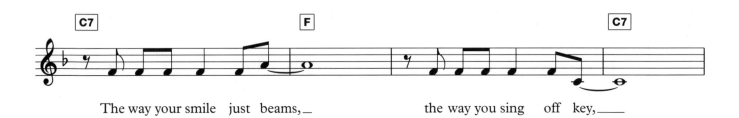

The way your smile just beams, __ the way you sing off key, ____

the way you haunt my dreams. No! No! They can't take that a-way from me.

__ We may ne-ver, ne-ver meet a-gain on the bum-py road to

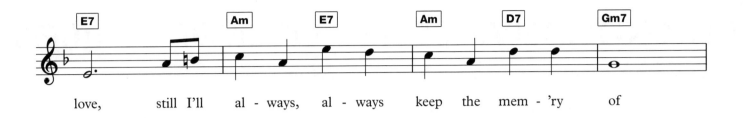

love,   still I'll   al - ways,   al - ways   keep   the   mem - 'ry   of

the way you hold your knife,___   the way we danced till   three,___

the way you've changed my life.___   No! No! They   can't take that a-way from me.

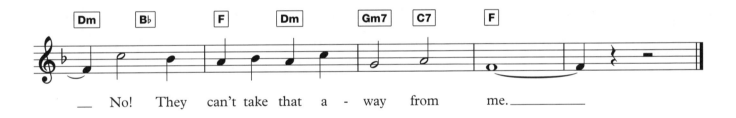

___   No!   They   can't take that   a - way   from   me._____

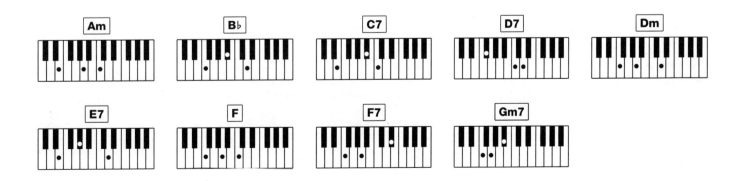

An expansive series of over 50 titles!

Each song features melody line, vocals, chord displays, suggested registrations and rhythm settings.

"For each title ALL the chords (both 3 finger and 4 finger) used are shown in the correct position - which makes a change!" **Organ & Keyboard Cavalcade, May 2001**

Each song appears on two facing pages eliminating the need to turn the page during performance. We have just introduced a new cover look to the series and will repackage the backlist in the same way.

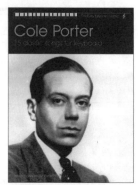

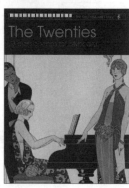

Big Band Hits	.19098
Blues	.3477A
Broadway	.9888A
Celebration Songs	.3478A
Christmas Carols	.4616A
Christmas Songs	.19198
Classic Hits Volume 1	.19099
Classic Hits Volume 2	.19100
Cliff Richard	.9030A
Cole Porter	.10041A
Country Songs	.19101
Disco	.9394A
Eighties, The	.2975A
Elton John	.5779A
English Favourites	.4229A
Favourite Hymns	.4179A
Fifties, The	.2972A
Film Classics	.19197
Forties, The	.2971A
Frank Sinatra	.9025A
George & Ira Gershwin	.9804A
George Michael	.7646A
Gilbert & Sullivan	.9707A
Glenn Miller	.5772A
Great Songwriters	.2225A
I Try Plus 10 More Chart Hits	.5778A
Instrumental Classics	.2338A
James Bond	.9236A
Jazz Classics	.5770A
Latin Collection	.5777A
Love Songs Volume 1	.19102
Love Songs Volume 2	.19199
Motown Classics	.2337A
Music Hall	.3329A
Nineties, The	.2976A
Number One Hits	.19200
Number One Hits Volume 2	.9787A
Popular Classics	.4180A
Pub Singalong Collection	.3954A
Queen	.9714A
Robbie Williams Easy Keyboard	.9501A
Rock 'n' Roll Classics	.2224A
Scott Joplin	.9738A
Seventies, The	.2974A
Shirley Bassey	.9350A
Showtunes Volume 1	.19103
Showtunes Volume 2	.3328A
Sixties, The	.2973A
Soft Rock Collection	.4617A
Soul Classics	.19201
Thirties, The	.2970A
Traditional English Favourites	.4229A
Traditional Irish Favourites	.4230A
Traditional Scottish Favourites	.4231A
TV Themes	.19196
Twenties, The	.2969A
Wartime Collection	.3955A
Wedding Collection	.3688A
Whitney Houston	.7647A